D1295958

PAGE 4

PAGE 5

PAGE 6

PAGE 7

PAGE 8

## PAGE 9

## PAGE 10

## PAGES 12 – 13

## PAGE 11

## PAGE 14

## PAGE 16

## PAGE 17

## PAGES 18 – 19

## PAGES 20 – 21

# PAGE 22

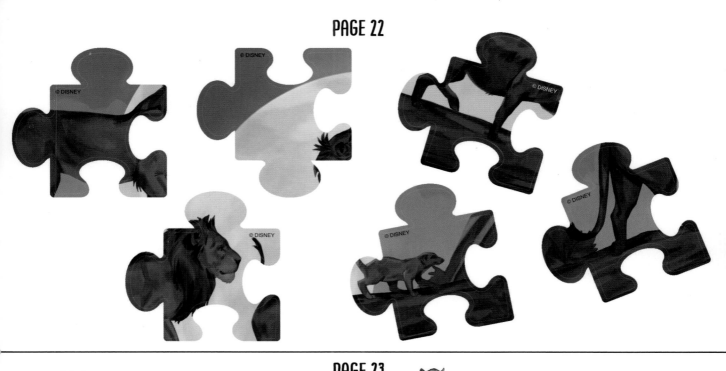

# PAGE 23

# PAGE 24

| 1 | 2 | 2 | 3 | 3 | 4 |

# PAGE 25

# PAGES 26 – 27

# PAGE 28

# PAGE 29

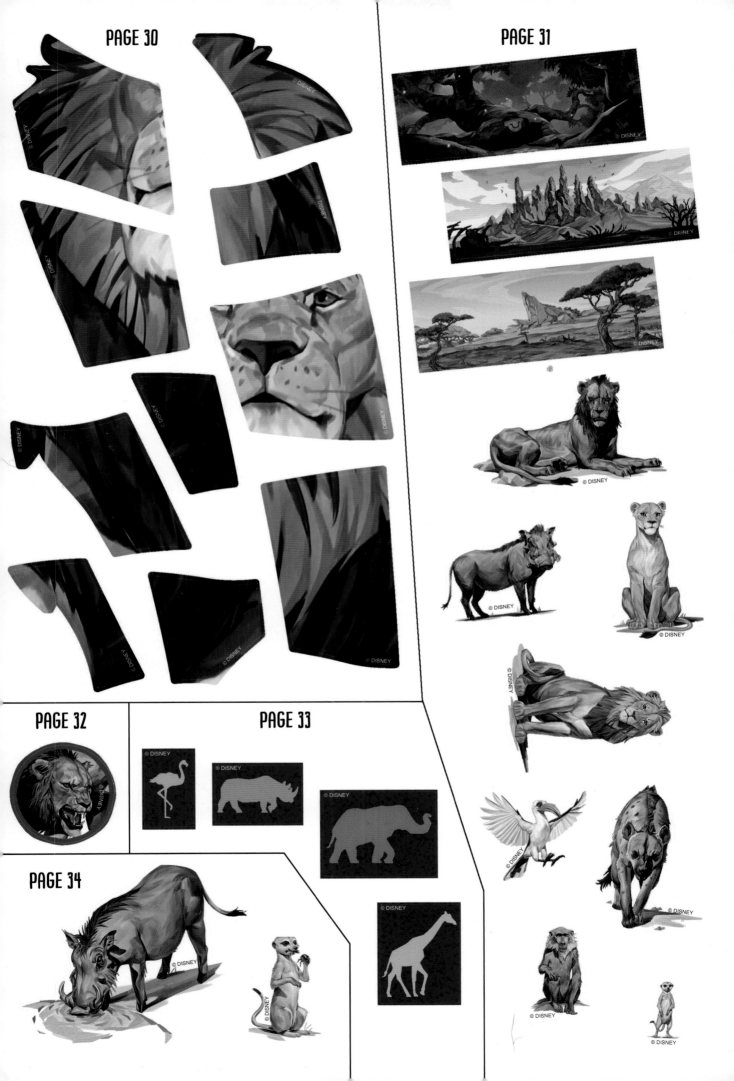

PAGE 30

PAGE 31

PAGE 32

PAGE 33

PAGE 34

EXTRA STICKERS

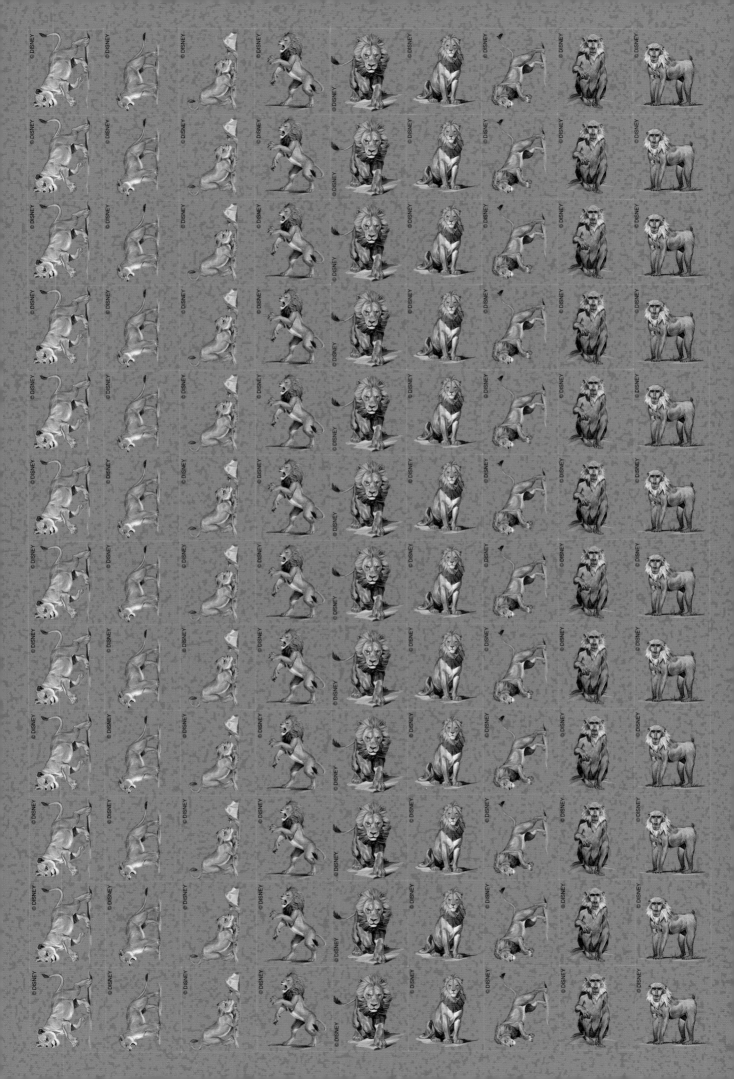

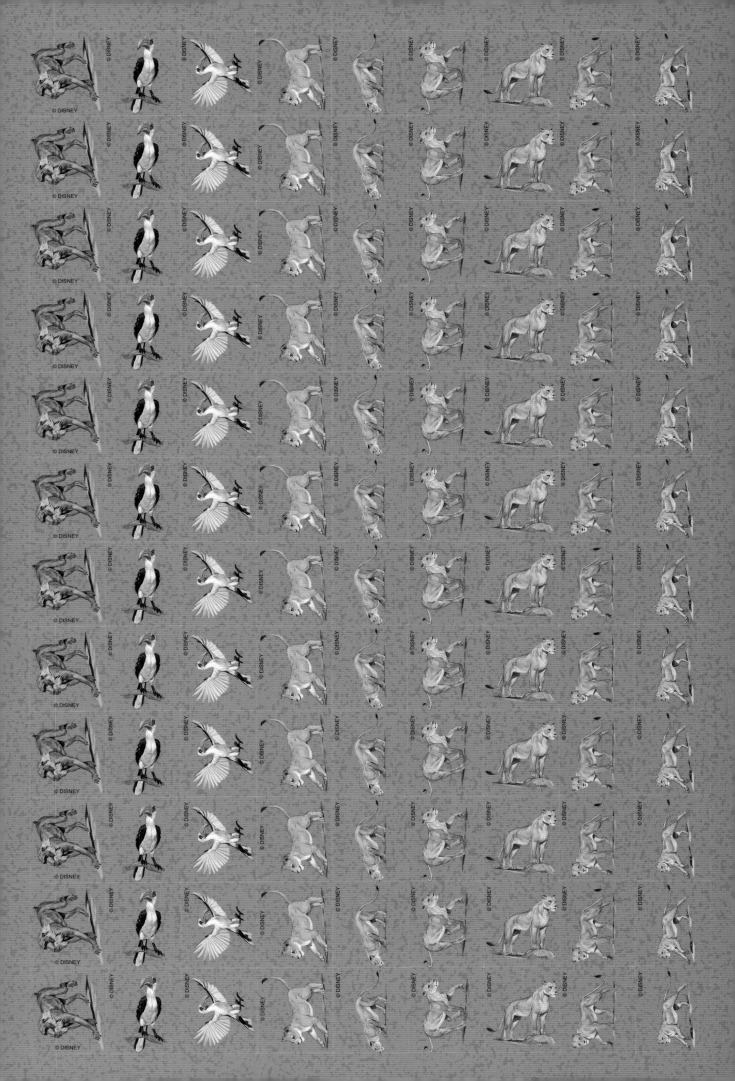

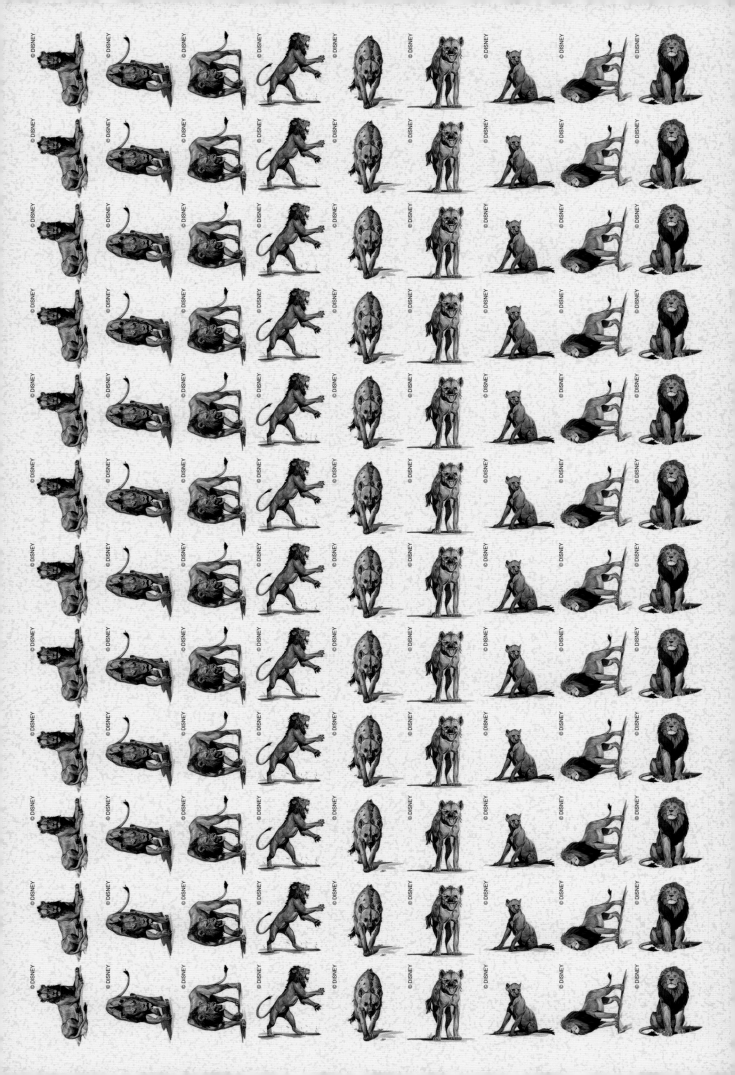

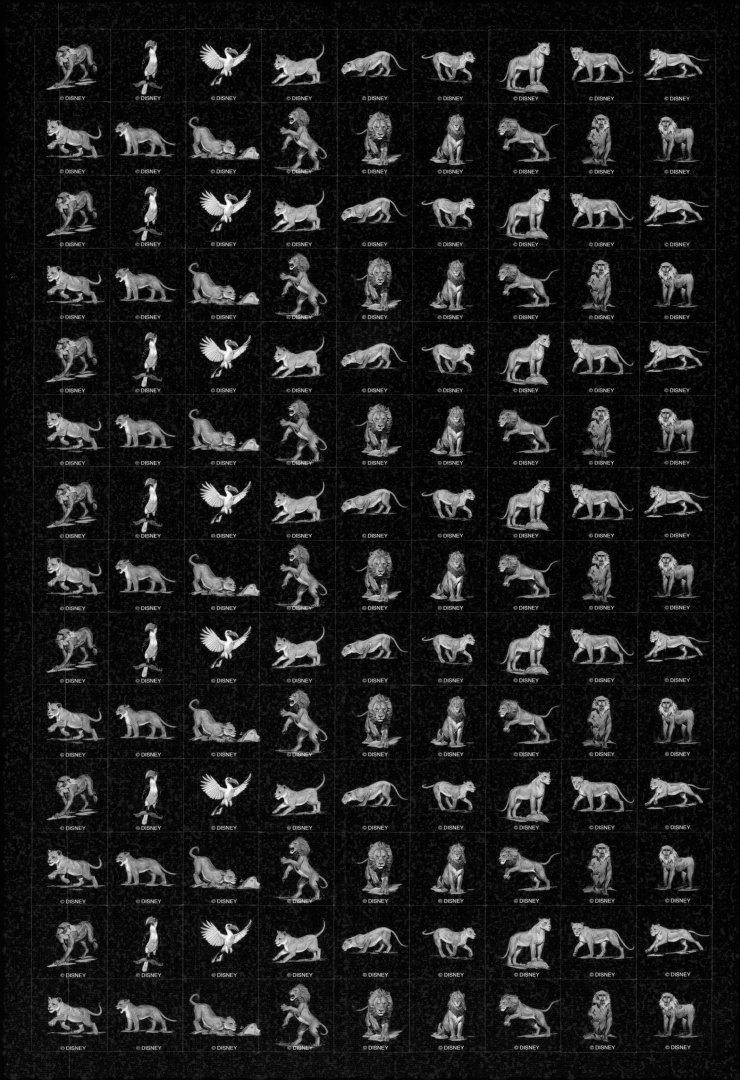

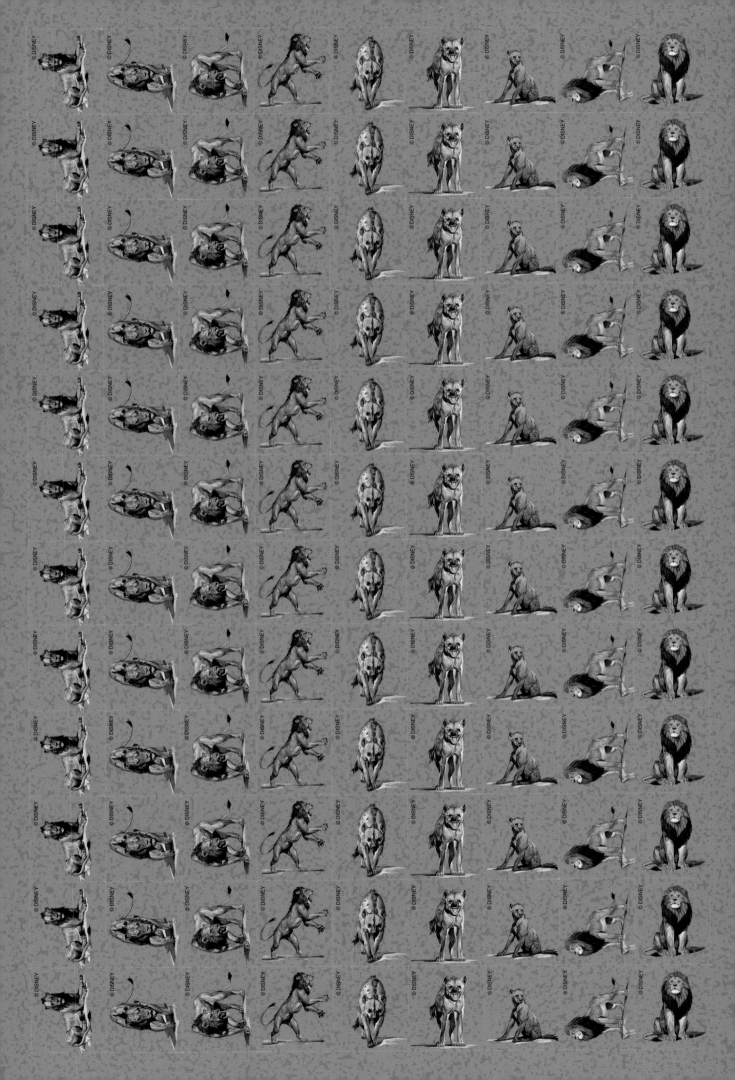

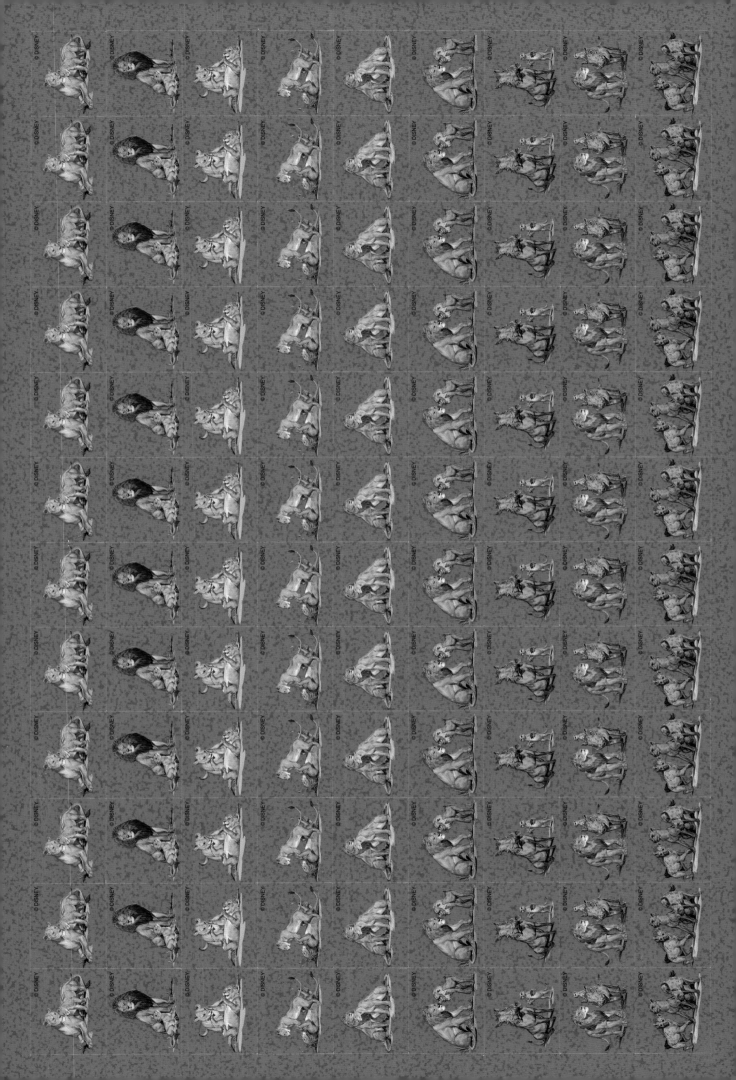

# DISNEY
# THE
# LION KING
# 1000 STICKER BOOK

DISNEY THE LION KING: 1000 STICKER BOOK
A CENTUM BOOK 978-1-913072-40-7
Published in Great Britain by Centum Books Ltd
This edition published 2019
1 3 5 7 9 10 8 6 4 2

Copyright © 2019 Disney Enterprises, Inc.

No part of this publication may be reproduced, stored in a retrieval system,
or transmitted in any form or by any means, electronic, mechanical, photocopying,
recording or otherwise, without the prior permission of the publishers.

Centum Books Ltd, 20 Devon Square, Newton Abbot, Devon, TQ12 2HR, UK

books@centumbooksltd.co.uk

CENTUM BOOKS Limited Reg. No. 07641486

A CIP catalogue record for this book is available from the British Library.

Printed in China.

# Centum

# SKETCH PRIDE ROCK

RAFIKI IS ON HIS WAY TO PRIDE ROCK, WHERE HE WILL PRESENT SIMBA, THE FUTURE KING OF THE PRIDE LANDS. WHAT DO YOU THINK PRIDE ROCK WOULD LOOK LIKE? ADD SOME ANIMAL STICKERS AND DRAW THE SCENE.

# HEIR TO THE THRONE

SARABI AND MUFASA ARE **TEACHING SIMBA** ABOUT HIS HOME. CAN YOU HELP LITTLE SIMBA KEEP UP? **STICK SIMBA IN PLACE** AND THEN **FIND THE TRAIL** OF LEAVES THAT WILL LEAD HIM THROUGH THE **PRIDE LANDS** TO HIS PROUD PARENTS.

A

B

C

D

# SPOTS AND STRIPES

MUFASA TEACHES SIMBA ABOUT THE IMPORTANCE OF RESPECTING ALL CREATURES. ADD STRIPES AND SPOTS TO EACH OF THESE UNIQUE ANIMALS IN THE PRIDE LANDS.

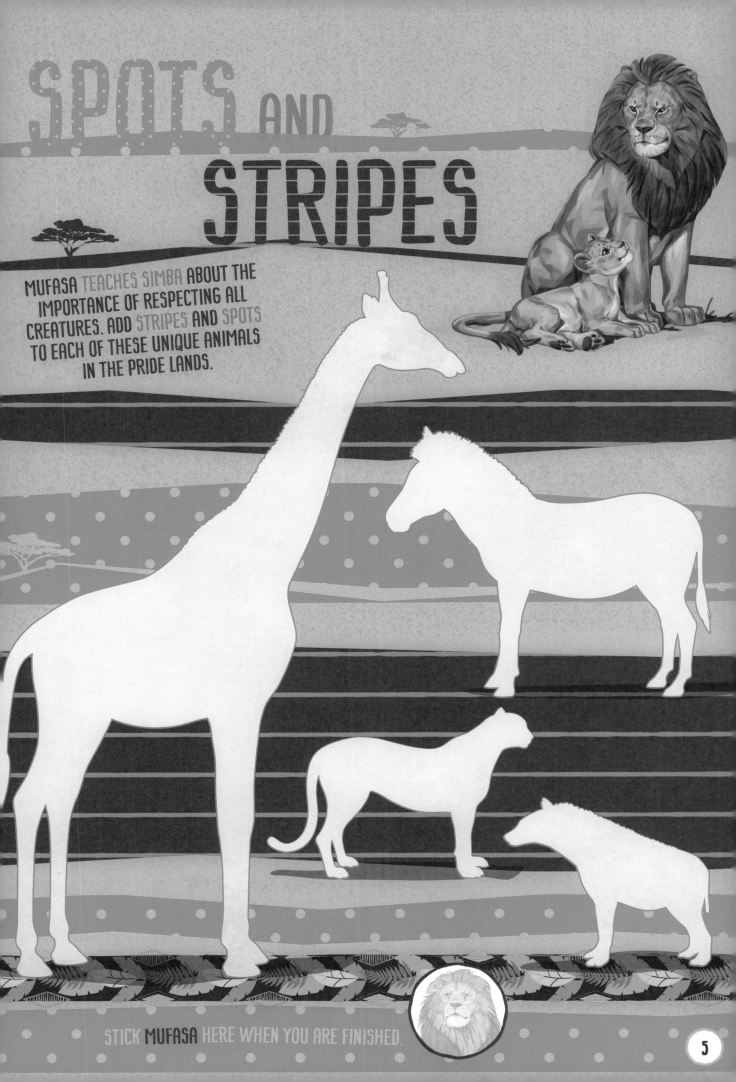

STICK MUFASA HERE WHEN YOU ARE FINISHED.

5

# WALK ON THE WILD SIDE

SIMBA AND NALA ARE TRYING TO SNEAK OFF TO THE ELEPHANT GRAVEYARD WITHOUT ZAZU SEEING THEM. CIRCLE THE 10 DIFFERENCES BETWEEN THESE TWO SCENES. CAN YOU FIND THEM ALL?

 STICK SIMBA HERE WHEN YOU ARE FINISHED.

# ESCAPE TUNNELS

THE CUBS REACH THE ELEPHANT GRAVEYARD, BUT THEY'RE SURROUNDED BY HYENAS!
HELP SIMBA AND NALA ESCAPE BY FINDING A ROUTE THROUGH THE TUNNELS.

START

STICK SIMBA AND NALA IN THE PRIDE LANDS
ONCE THEY HAVE ESCAPED.

FINISH

ANSWERS ON PAGE 39

# A KING'S ADVICE

USE THE SYMBOLS TO DECODE WHAT MUFASA TELLS SIMBA ABOUT THE GREAT KINGS OF THE PAST. WRITE THE DECODED LETTERS IN THE STARS.

STICK MUFASA HERE WHEN YOU ARE FINISHED.

# CAN'T WAIT TO BE KING

ZAZU WILL BE HAPPY TO SEE SIMBA ON THE THRONE OF PRIDE ROCK, BUT HE KNOWS THE FUTURE KING STILL HAS MUCH TO LEARN. CAN YOU HELP SIMBA WITH HIS ROYAL TRAINING? USE THE KEY AND YOUR STICKERS TO COMPLETE THE SUMS BELOW.

**KEY:** 1    2    3    4

     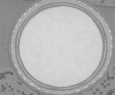

  +    =

  +   =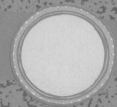

  -  +  =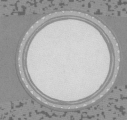

# PAWFUL OF FUN

SIMBA AND NALA ARE RACING TO SEE WHO CAN REACH THE HEAD OF A VALLEY. WITH A FRIEND, SEE WHO CAN FINISH THE PUZZLE AND REACH THE TOP FIRST. WITH A PENCIL, TRACE INSIDE THE PATHS BELOW AS FAST AS YOU CAN WITHOUT TOUCHING THE SIDES. STOP AT EACH OBSTACLE AND COMPLETE THE ACTIVITY, THEN KEEP TRACING. THE FIRST PERSON TO REACH THE FINISH LINE WINS!

## START

PENCILS DOWN! STAND UP AND DO FIVE STAR JUMPS.

STOP TRACING! COUNT TO **20** AS FAST AS YOU CAN.

ALMOST THERE! RUN TO THE END OF THE ROOM AND BACK AGAIN.

STOP TRACING! COUNT TO **20** AS FAST AS YOU CAN.

STICK THE WINNER HERE!

## FINISH

# HEAR ME ROAR!

SIMBA IS PRACTICING HIS MIGHTY ROAR. WHICH ROAR IS THE LOUDEST? USE YOUR STICKERS TO NUMBER THE ROARS FROM 1 TO 5, WITH 1 AS THE SMALLEST AND 5 AS THE BIGGEST.

ROAR

ROAR

ROAR

ROAR

ROAR

# SARABI VS SCAR

WHEN SCAR TAKES MUFASA'S PLACE AS KING, SARABI CONFRONTS HIM. WHAT DO YOU THINK WOULD HAPPEN NEXT? TELL THE STORY IN THE BOXES BELOW WITH WORDS OR DRAWINGS.

WHO WILL WIN – SARABI OR SCAR?
STICK YOUR CHOICE HERE.

# TAKIN' IT EASY

WHEN SIMBA RUNS AWAY FROM THE PRIDE LANDS, HE MAKES TWO NEW FRIENDS, TIMON AND PUMBAA. CAN YOU HELP TIMON SNIFF OUT HIS WARTHOG FRIEND? FOLLOW THE MUDDY TRAIL TO FIND PUMBAA.

A

B

C

STICK PUMBAA HERE WHEN YOU FIND THE RIGHT PATH.

ANSWERS ON PAGE 39

# LET'S PLAY!

SIMBA'S LIFE WITH HIS NEWFOUND **FRIENDS** IS ALL ABOUT HAVING FUN. CUT OUT THE **CHARACTERS** BELOW, THEN ACT OUT YOUR OWN FUN SCENES.

1. ASK AN ADULT TO HELP YOU CUT ALONG THE DOTTED LINES, AND ALONG THE SLOT LINES.
2. GLUE YOUR CHARACTERS ONTO CARD STOCK SO THEY'LL STAND UP.
3. ASSEMBLE YOUR CHARACTERS BY PLACING THEM IN THE STANDS. · · · · · · · · · · · · ·>

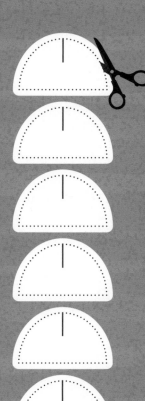

© Disney

© Disney

COMPLETE THE NEXT PAGE BEFORE YOU START CUTTING.

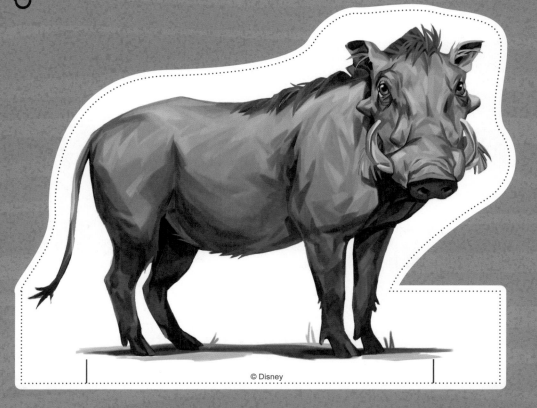

© Disney

# PUT YOUR ROAR INTO IT

MAKE UP YOUR OWN LYRICS TO THE *TUNE* OF
YOUR FAVOURITE *THE LION KING* SONG.
THEN SING IT FOR YOUR FAMILY AND FRIENDS!

STICK **SIMBA** HERE WHEN YOU ARE FINISHED.

# GRAB GRUB!

TIMON AND PUMBAA ARE CHOOSING THE TASTIEST BUG FOR SIMBA. HELP THEM PICK THE CORRECT BUG BASED ON THE HINTS.

1. THE BUG IS NOT RED.

2. THE BUG HAS MORE THAN TWO LEGS.

3. THE BUG'S BODY IS MORE THAN ONE SHAPE.

4. THE BUG HAS THE COLOUR OF THE SUN IN IT.

STICK THE CORRECT BUG HERE.

ANSWERS ON PAGE 39

# READY TO POUNCE!

SIMBA IS LEARNING HOW TO CATCH BUGS IN THE CLOUD FOREST. CAN YOU HELP HIM CATCH ENOUGH GRUB FOR DINNER? PLAY THIS GAME WITH A FRIEND. WHOEVER REACHES TIMON AND PUMBAA FIRST WINS!

**10**

**9**
OOH, EXTRA CRUNCHY. GO FORWARD TWO SPACES.

**7**

**15**
YUM! YOU FOUND TIMON'S FAVOURITE BUG. TAKE ANOTHER TURN.

**12**
OOPS, YOU MISSED A BUG! GO BACK ONE SPACE TO CATCH IT.

**13**

**16**

**17**

## HOW TO PLAY
1. USE YOUR STICKERS TO COMPLETE THE BOARD.
2. PUT BOTH YOUR COINS ON START.
3. TAKE TURNS ROLLING THE DIE AND MOVING ALONG THE PATH.
4. FOLLOW ANY INSTRUCTIONS YOU LAND ON.
5. THE FIRST PERSON TO REACH THE FINISH WINS!

YOU WILL NEED:
2 COINS
1 DICE
A FRIEND TO
PLAY WITH!

START

2

5

4
THAT'S SOME
GOOD-LOOKIN' GRUB.
POUNCE FORWARD
ONE SPACE.

6
YUCK! THAT BUG'S
WAY TOO SLIMY.
MISS A TURN.

19

FINISH

18
YOUR MIGHTY ROAR
SCARED ALL THE BUGS
AWAY! MISS A TURN.

# ANIMAL INSTINCT

WHICH CHARACTER ARE YOU MOST LIKE? TAKE THIS QUIZ TO FIND OUT AND THEN ADD A SUN STICKER NEXT TO YOUR CHARACTER!

DO YOU PREFER **GOOD** OVER **EVIL**?

NO

YES

WOULD YOU **EAT A BUG**?

YES

IF I **HAD** TO...

BOOKWORM

LIKE SIMBA, YOU ARE EAGER TO PLEASE. YOU MAY BE AFRAID OF YOUR OWN DESTINY — DON'T SHY AWAY FROM WHO YOU WERE MEANT TO BE!

IF YOU GOT RAFIKI, YOU ARE VERY WISE. YOU GIVE GREAT ADVICE TO ALL YOUR FRIENDS AND KNOW THE IMPORTANCE OF BEING TRUE TO YOURSELF.

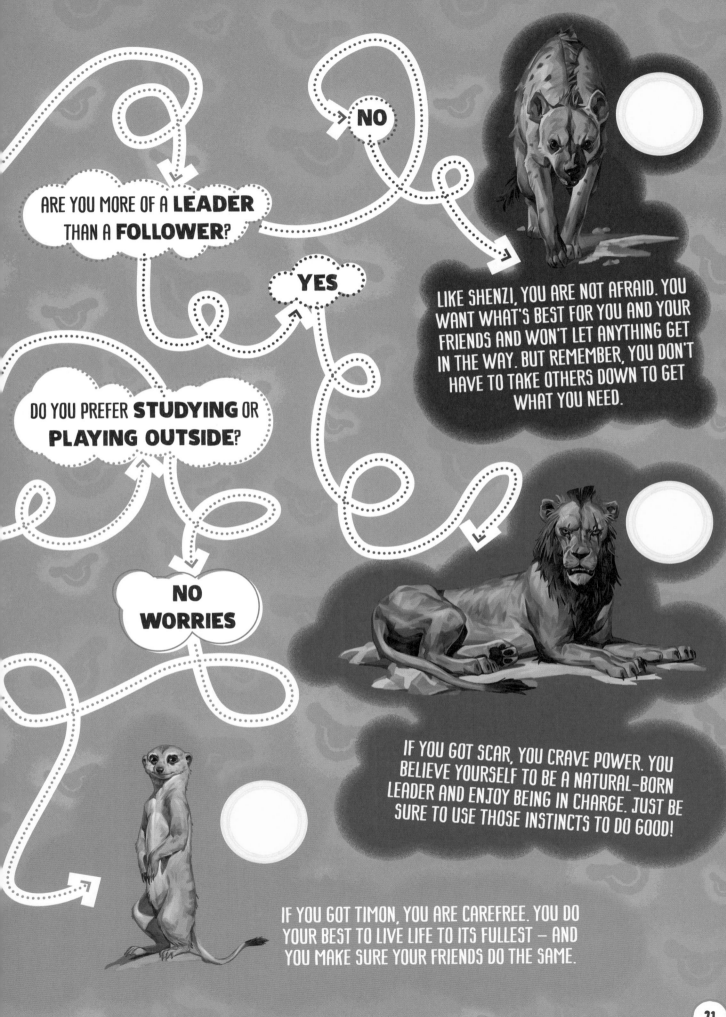

ARE YOU MORE OF A **LEADER** THAN A **FOLLOWER**?

NO

YES

LIKE SHENZI, YOU ARE NOT AFRAID. YOU WANT WHAT'S BEST FOR YOU AND YOUR FRIENDS AND WON'T LET ANYTHING GET IN THE WAY. BUT REMEMBER, YOU DON'T HAVE TO TAKE OTHERS DOWN TO GET WHAT YOU NEED.

DO YOU PREFER **STUDYING** OR **PLAYING OUTSIDE**?

NO WORRIES

IF YOU GOT SCAR, YOU CRAVE POWER. YOU BELIEVE YOURSELF TO BE A NATURAL-BORN LEADER AND ENJOY BEING IN CHARGE. JUST BE SURE TO USE THOSE INSTINCTS TO DO GOOD!

IF YOU GOT TIMON, YOU ARE CAREFREE. YOU DO YOUR BEST TO LIVE LIFE TO ITS FULLEST — AND YOU MAKE SURE YOUR FRIENDS DO THE SAME.

# NO WORRIES

AS SIMBA GROWS INTO A BIG, STRONG LION, TIMON AND PUMBAA TEACH HIM HOW TO LIVE A WORRY-FREE LIFE. USE YOUR STICKERS TO COMPLETE THE JIGSAW SCENE.

# TRICKSTERS IN THE WILD

A PACK OF HYENAS IS CROUCHED IN HIDING, WAITING TO TRICK NALA! STICK SOME MORE HYENAS ON THE SCENE AND THEN COUNT THEM ALL SO THAT NALA CAN BE ON HER GUARD.

THERE ARE

HYENAS

ANSWERS ON PAGE 39

NALA PROWLS THROUGH THE CLOUD FOREST, SLOWLY SNEAKING UP ON AN UNSUSPECTING SIMBA. HOW MANY OF EACH OF THESE PLANTS AND ANIMALS CAN SHE SEE THROUGH THE TREES? STICK THE CORRECT NUMBER IN EACH BOX.

# LONGTIME FRIENDS

NALA PINS SIMBA, AND THEY REALISE THEY KNOW EACH OTHER! HAVE YOU EVER BEEN REUNITED WITH A FRIEND OR A FAMILY MEMBER AFTER A LONG TIME? WHAT WAS IT LIKE? WRITE ABOUT IT HERE.

STICK NALA HERE WHEN YOU ARE FINISHED.

# RACE FOR PRIDE ROCK

NALA WANTS SIMBA TO RETURN TO THE PRIDE LANDS AND TAKE HIS RIGHTFUL PLACE AS KING. BUT SIMBA WANTS TO STAY IN THE CLOUD FOREST. WHICH LION DO YOU AGREE WITH?

GRAB A FRIEND, PICK A TEAM, AND COMPLETE THE MAZES AT THE SAME TIME. WHOEVER FINISHES FIRST, WINS!

STICK NALA AND SIMBA IN PLACE BEFORE YOU BEGIN AND USE A PENCIL SO YOU CAN PLAY AGAIN.

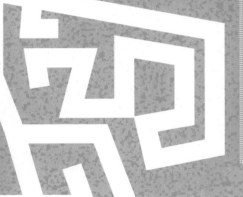

# RAFIKI'S RIDDLES

SIMBA HEARS A FAMILIAR LAUGH ECHOING THROUGH THE TREES. IT'S RAFIKI! HE HAS LOTS OF WISE — AND SOMETIMES CONFUSING — ADVICE TO SHARE. CAN YOU HELP SIMBA WORK OUT THESE PUZZLING RIDDLES?

**1** WHAT JUMPS WHEN IT WALKS AND SITS WHEN IT STANDS?

**2** WHAT KIND OF ANIMAL CAN JUMP HIGHER THAN A TREE?

**3** WHAT DOES A LION BECOME AFTER IT IS THREE DAYS OLD?

**4** WHAT GROWS UP WHILE GROWING DOWN?

**5** WHAT'S AS BIG AS AN ELEPHANT, BUT WEIGHS NOTHING AT ALL?

STICK RAFIKI HERE WHEN YOU ARE FINISHED.

# A LION'S LESSON

WHEN SIMBA SEES MUFASA'S REFLECTION IN THE WATER, HE REMEMBERS ONE OF HIS FATHER'S MOST IMPORTANT LESSONS. STICK MUFASA IN PLACE AND THEN CROSS OUT EVERY SECOND LETTER AROUND THE CIRCLE TO COMPLETE HIS WISE WORDS. FINALLY, WRITE THE LESSON INSIDE THE CIRCLE.

## "YOU MUST TAKE YOUR PLACE IN THE . . ."

FGECGAR SEBAZTDCPIMRKCOLOEXQQFPLOIZ

..........................................................

..........................................................

..........................................................

# GREAT KINGS
## OF THE PAST

SIMBA SEES A VISION OF HIS FATHER IN THE STORM CLOUDS.

USE YOUR STICKERS TO COMPLETE THE PICTURE AND SHOW MUFASA'S FACE IN THE SKY.

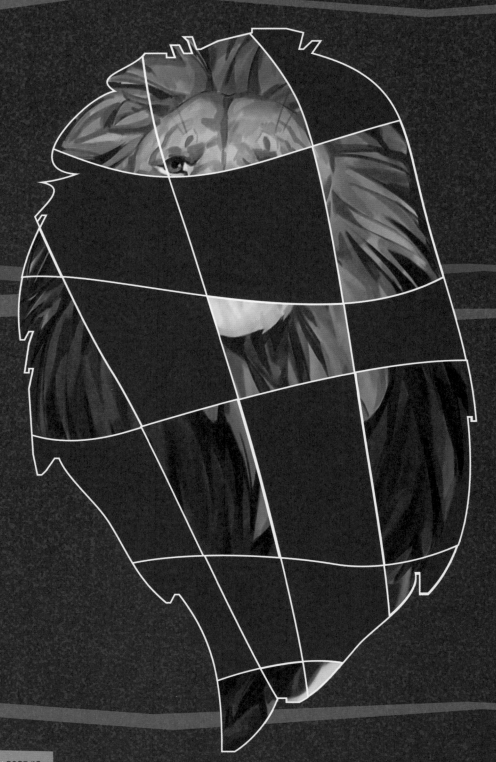

ANSWERS ON PAGE 40

# ADVENTURE AWAITS!

SIMBA AND HIS FRIENDS GO ON AN ADVENTURE BACK TO THE PRIDE LANDS. IMAGINE YOU'RE TAKING AN AMAZING JOURNEY WITH YOUR FRIENDS AND COMPLETE THE ADVENTURE JOURNAL BELOW.

STICK YOUR CHOICE OF LOCATION BELOW.

WHO'S YOUR ADVENTURE BUDDY? WRITE A FRIEND'S NAME HERE.

WHICH ANIMAL FRIEND WILL YOU TAKE WITH YOU?
STICK YOUR FAVOURITE BELOW.

WHO WILL YOU ENCOUNTER ALONG THE WAY? STICK YOUR CHOICE BELOW

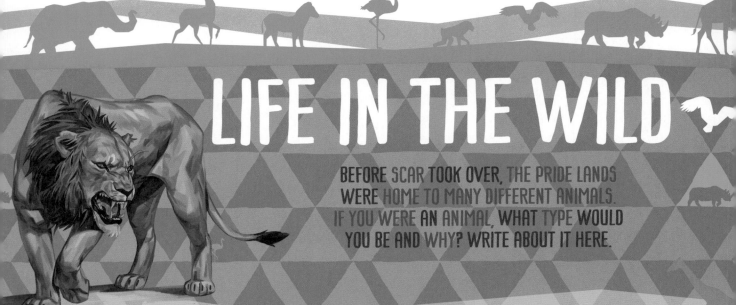

# LIFE IN THE WILD

BEFORE SCAR TOOK OVER, THE PRIDE LANDS WERE HOME TO MANY DIFFERENT ANIMALS. IF YOU WERE AN ANIMAL, WHAT TYPE WOULD YOU BE AND WHY? WRITE ABOUT IT HERE.

STICK SCAR HERE WHEN YOU ARE FINISHED.

# SAVANNAH STAMPEDE

THE ANIMALS OF THE PRIDE LANDS MARCH THROUGH THE SAVANNAH AS THEY AWAIT THE RETURN OF SIMBA, THEIR ONE TRUE KING. COMPLETE THE SEQUENCES BELOW BY STICKING THE RIGHT ANIMALS IN THE EMPTY SPACES BELOW.

# HYENA HUSTLE

HELP TIMON AND PUMBAA DISTRACT SHENZI, AZIZI AND KAMARI SO SIMBA CAN REACH SCAR. FOLLOW THE DIRECTIONS TO LURE THE HYENAS TOWARDS TIMON AND PUMBAA AND AWAY FROM PRIDE ROCK.

KEY

UP   DOWN   LEFT   RIGHT

START

FINISH

STICK TIMON AND PUMBAA HERE WHEN YOU REACH THEM.

# ONE TRUE KING

THE PRIDE LANDS ARE FINALLY RID OF SCAR, AND SIMBA TAKES HIS RIGHTFUL PLACE AS KING. FIND AND CIRCLE THE ANIMALS WHO ARE HAPPY TO HAVE SIMBA BACK. LOOK IN EVERY DIRECTION, INCLUDING DIAGONAL.

ANTELOPE
CHEETAH

ZEBRA
ELEPHANT

FLAMINGOS
HORNBILL

LION
RHINO

STORK
WARTHOG

```
A N T E L O P E L E P H
M R I L I N O I I O L I
I C N E O H O N E A W N
N H O R N B I L L K R O
G E I E E T H Z E B A D
Z E B R A A B E P Z W K
U T I B W A R T H O G L
Q A N Z K E A S A T C I
R H G A P R K O N I H R
A G O R B I O R T T E K
O N N B L I H T H O E O
F L A M I N G O S G H S
```

STICK SIMBA HERE WHEN YOU ARE FINISHED.

ANSWERS ON PAGE 40

35

# HEART OF A LION

SIMBA **AND** NALA **HAVE GROWN UP TO BE** BIG, STRONG LIONS. DO YOU WANT TO BE BIG AND STRONG **LIKE** SIMBA AND NALA? GRAB A DICE **AND GET MOVING!**

IF YOU ROLL A 1 . . . DO 10 STAR JUMPS!

IF YOU ROLL A 2 . . . STRETCH YOUR ARMS UP AND REACH FOR THE STARS.

IF YOU ROLL A 3 . . . REACH DOWN LOW AND TOUCH YOUR TOES.

IF YOU ROLL A 4 . . . HOP, SKIP AND JUMP THREE TIMES.

IF YOU ROLL A 5 . . . BALANCE ON ONE LEG FOR AS LONG AS YOU CAN, THEN SWAP LEGS!

IF YOU ROLL A 6 . . . RACE A FRIEND. READY, STEADY, GO!

STICK SIMBA HERE WHEN YOU ARE FINISHED.

# A FUTURE LEADER

RAFIKI RETURNS TO PRIDE ROCK TO PRESENT ANOTHER LION CUB TO THE ANIMAL KINGDOM — SIMBA AND NALA'S LITTLE ONE! PAINT YOUR OWN PORTRAIT OF THE NEW CUB.

YOU WILL NEED:
YELLOW, ORANGE
AND BROWN PAINT
A PAINTBRUSH

STICK SIMBA HERE WHEN YOU ARE FINISHED.

# SLAYIN' IT

TEST YOUR KNOWLEDGE OF *THE LION KING* BY ANSWERING THE QUESTIONS BELOW. ADD AN **A OR B** ANSWER STICKER FOR EACH QUESTION.

**1. THE CIRCLE OF LIFE IS:**
A. A GIANT ROAD THAT GOES AROUND THE ENTIRE WORLD.
B. THE BALANCE AND RESPECT OF ALL CREATURES.

**2. IT IS IMPORTANT TO BE TRUE TO YOURSELF.**
A. TRUE
B. FALSE

**3. ACCORDING TO PUMBAA, THE STARS ARE:**
A. THE GREAT KINGS OF THE PAST
B. GIANT BALLS OF BURNING GAS, BILLIONS OF MILES AWAY

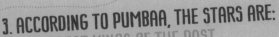

**4. TIMON AND PUMBAA LIKE TO SPEND THEIR TIME:**
A. TAKING IT EASY
B. WORRYING

**5. MUFASA IS PROUD OF HIS SON.**
A. TRUE
B. FALSE

**6. SIMBA IS THE RIGHTFUL KING OF PRIDE ROCK.**
A. TRUE
B. FALSE

ANSWERS ON **PAGE 40**

# ANSWERS

PAGE 4: B

PAGE 6:

PAGE 7:

START

FINISH

PAGE 8: THEY WATCH OVER US FROM THE STARS.

PAGE 9:

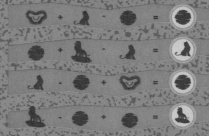

PAGE 11: 1; 5; 4; 2; 3

PAGE 14: B

PAGE 17:

PAGE 22:

PAGE 23:
25 HYENAS

PAGE 24:

| 2 | 3 | 1 | 2 | 4 | 3 |

PAGES 26 – 27:

PAGE 28: 1 – A FROG; 2 – ANY ANIMAL. TREES CAN'T JUMP; 3 – FOUR DAYS OLD; 4 – A GOOSE; 5 – AN ELEPHANT'S SHADOW

PAGE 29: GREAT CIRCLE OF LIFE

# ANSWERS

PAGE 30:

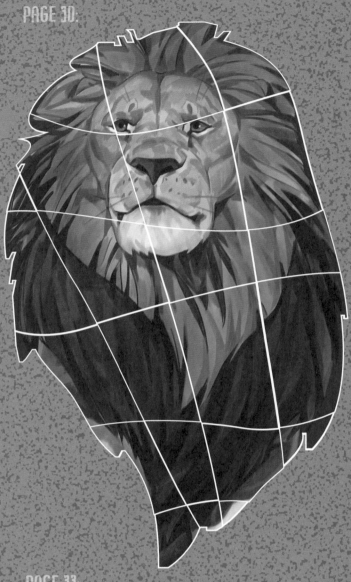

PAGE 34:

PAGE 35:

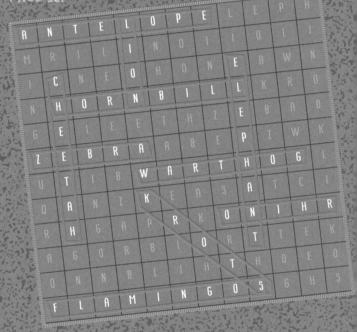

PAGE 38: 1 – B, 2 – A, 3 – B, 4 – A, 5 – A, 6 – A

PAGE 33:

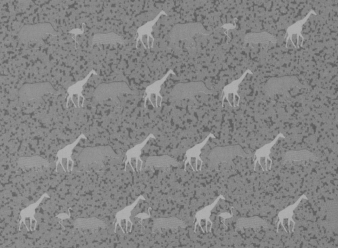